This igloo book belongs to:

Ada, with love
on your 2nd
birthday!

Contents

igloobooks

Published in 2023
First published in the UK by Igloo Books Ltd
An imprint of Igloo Books Ltd
Cottage Farm, NN6 0BJ, UK
Owned by Bonnier Books
Sveavägen 56, Stockholm, Sweden
www.igloobooks.com

0223 004
4 6 8 10 9 7 5 3
ISBN 978-1-80368-037-8

Written by Everley Hart
Illustrated by Kristen Humphrey

Designed by Hannah George
Edited by James Phoenix

Printed and manufactured in China

Five-Minute
STORIES
FOR
2 YEAR OLDS

igloobooks

Garden Adventure

Leela sees a **flutter**. Whatever could it be?

Grandad says,

A butterfly! We've got to set it free.

4

Grandad, can I keep it? But Grandad shakes his head.

All of nature's wildlife belongs out there instead.

He opens up the window,
and he cups it in his hands.

When Leela sees it **fly** away,
she starts to understand.

So, they pick up **prickly** pine cones,
then gather twigs and leaves...

... to make the bugs a home,
before they give the birds some seeds.

Leela plants some flowers
for the bees to **buzz** around,
while Grandad makes some compost
for the creatures on the ground.

Soon, the sun is setting.

Is there more that we can do?

So, they fill a bowl with water for the night-time hedgehogs too.

Then, early in the morning, when the birds begin their song,
Leela sees that everything is right where it belongs.

Jump and Hop

Can you **gallop** round the garden?

Can you catch a **bouncy** ball?

Can you **pedal** on your tricycle
and not get scared at all?

13

Can you **balance** like an acrobat performing in a show?

Can you **jump** high on the trampoline?

Woo-hoo, look at you go!

Can you **hop-hop** like a bunny when you're playing with your friends?

What will you learn next?
The playtime fun will never end.

Roar Like a Lion

Whenever you're angry and ready to shout...

...ROAR like a lion to let it all out!

Or, if you're sad and have tears in your eyes...

... HOWL

like a wolf does. It's okay to cry.

You can **SING** like a bird.

You can **BUZZ** like a bee.

Happy or **sad,** just join in and see!

23

Chattering Charlie

Chattering Charlie has so much to say
that he doesn't stop talking all night and all day.

He talks to his toys as
he lies in his cot.

Yes, Charlie likes
chattering quite a lot!

25

But one day he finds that he's **run out of words!**

He looks for some new ones, and what does he see?

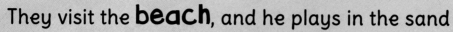

They visit the **beach**, and he plays in the sand

with a **bucket** for castles and

spade

in his hand.

He learns words at the **farmyard** and words in the **shops**.

Charlie learns so many words... **HE CAN'T STOP!**

29

Learning to Fly

When we're at the park, there is so much to do.

I love to bounce **high** on the see-saw with you.

He learns words at the **farmyard** and words in the **shops**.

Charlie learns so many words... **HE CAN'T STOP!**

Learning to Fly

When we're at the park, there is so much to do.

I love to bounce **high** on the see-saw with you.

We play on the swings.

Let's go really high!

Then, we see somebody learning to **fly!**

I wave to the girl and ask,

What have you there?

She says,

It's my kite, and it soars through the air!

She hands me the string as
the wind starts to **blow**.

It gets a lot stronger and then... **I let go!**

It **loopity-loops**
and gets caught in a tree...

... so, she helps me climb
up to pull the kite free.

I hand it right back and say,

Look, good as new!

Then we share a **tasty** ice cream made for two.

Benny's Bath Time

Come and meet Benny, a nice little lad
who's lovely all day, but at bath time he's **BAD**.

He's scared when the water is **rushing** and **flowing**
and runs off to hide without anyone knowing.

He's sure there's a creature that **lurks** in the deep
with terrible **tentacles** ready to creep.

What if a wave comes to **wash** him to sea?

Or he's sucked down the plughole and **eaten** for tea?

One day, when Mummy says,

Benny, inside!

He finds in the bathroom
a **big water slide!**

The water's so **bubbly**, his toys are such fun
that Benny likes baths more than **anyone!**

A Monster Like Me

There's a monster in my bedroom!

Lucy whispers every night...

... as she hides under the covers, scared and trembling with fright.

Grandma sits beside her,
and she kisses Lucy's head.

There's no one hiding in your
room or underneath your bed.

43

She tells her that it's bedtime for the little monsters too.

They're sleeping in their monster bedrooms, just like YOU!

Their monster parents tell them that it's time to go upstairs,
put on their pyjamas and comb their monster hair.

They brush their
monster teeth
until they **sparkle**
monster clean.

They read a monster story
and they **dream** a monster dream.

But even little monsters
feel frightened on their own...

... so, dream of your friend monster,
and you'll never be alone!